FAMILY ENTERTAINMENT NETWORK, INC.™

JOSEPH IN EGYPT

COLORING & ACTIVITY BOOK

From the Animated Stories From the OLD TESTAMENT

Series I

D1385285

By: Laurie Bonnell Stephens

Assisted By: Melissa Johns
Illustrated By: John Dubiel
Cover Design: Randy Clark

THE FAMILY ENTERTAINMENT NETWORK'S COLORING AND ACTIVITY BOOK

The purpose of this book is to help individuals, families, and groups alike learn to use the Bible in conjunction with the **"Joseph in Egypt"** video from the Family Entertainment Network's Animated Stories from the Old Testament video series. The book is divided into three main sections; the **"Pictures to Color Section"**, the **"Questions, Games, & Activities Section"**, and the **"Answer Key"**.

SCRIPTURAL REFERENCES. The Scriptural Reference page contains a comprehensive, alphabetical listing of the scriptural topics and principles that are found in the animated story. After each topic is listed, you will find the biblical reference or references where each topic or principle can be found.

POINTS TO PONDER. There are no answers indicated for "Points To Ponder" in the Answer Key. We have included these questions for the sole purpose of allowing both children and adults to think deeply about these topics.

Although most of the answers to each activity can be found by watching the **"Joseph in Egypt"** video, the Bible is another great source to find the answers. We strongly suggest that you spend time reading and discussing the Biblical account of **"Joseph in Egypt"** with your child or family. For scriptural information in finding answers to questions and games in this activity book, please see **Genesis 37:36** and **Genesis Chapters 39-41.**

Family Entertainment Network hopes that this Coloring and Activity Book will make your investment in the Animated Stories from the Old Testament become even more valuable as you study the scriptures and become better acquainted with the stories from the Bible.

Printed in the United States of America

TABLE OF CONTENTS

REFERENCES

JOSEPH IN EGYPT

Pictures to Color

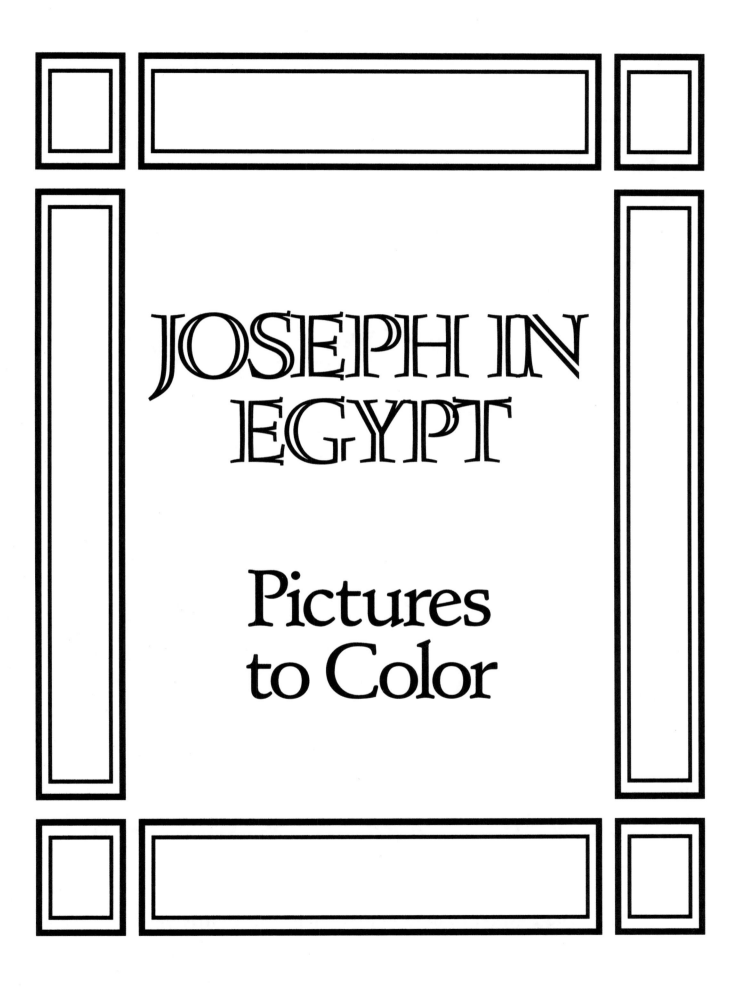

The Egyptian Pharaoh dreams a strange dream.

Genesis 41:1-7

Family Entertainment Network, Inc.™ • P.O. Box 550759 • Dallas, Texas 75355-0759

The mystic cannot interpret Pharaoh's dream.

Genesis 41:8

Family Entertainment Network, Inc.™ • P.O. Box 550759 • Dallas, Texas 75355-0759

“Is there no one in Egypt who can interpret dreams?”

see Genesis 41:8

Family Entertainment Network, Inc.™ • P.O. Box 550759 • Dallas, Texas 75355-0759

"I know someone who can interpret your dreams."

Genesis 41:9-13

Joseph is sold as a slave in Egypt.

Genesis 37:36; Genesis 39:1

Family Entertainment Network, Inc.™ • P.O. Box 550759 • Dallas, Texas 75355-0759

Potiphar purchases Joseph as a servant.

Genesis 37:36; Genesis 39:1

Joseph serves Potiphar well.

Genesis 39:1-6

Family Entertainment Network, Inc.™ • P.O. Box 550759 • Dallas, Texas 75355-0759

Joseph escapes from Potiphar's wife.

Genesis 39:7-12

Potiphar's wife tells lies about Joseph.

Genesis 39:13-19

Family Entertainment Network, Inc.™ • P.O. Box 550759 • Dallas, Texas 75355-0759

Potiphar casts Joseph into prison.

Genesis 39:20

The jailkeeper gains trust in Joseph.

Genesis 39:21-23

Family Entertainment Network, Inc.™ • P.O. Box 550759 • Dallas, Texas 75355-0759

Joseph interprets the dreams of the butler and baker.

Genesis 40:5-22

Joseph interprets the Pharaoh's dream.

Genesis 41:14-32

Family Entertainment Network, Inc.™ • P.O. Box 550759 • Dallas, Texas 75355-0759

Joseph tells the Pharaoh how to prepare for the approaching famine.

Genesis 41:33-36

Joseph is appointed as ruler over Egypt by the Pharaoh.

Genesis 41:39-43

Family Entertainment Network, Inc.™ • P.O. Box 550759 • Dallas, Texas 75355-0759

JOSEPH IN EGYPT

Questions, Games & Activities

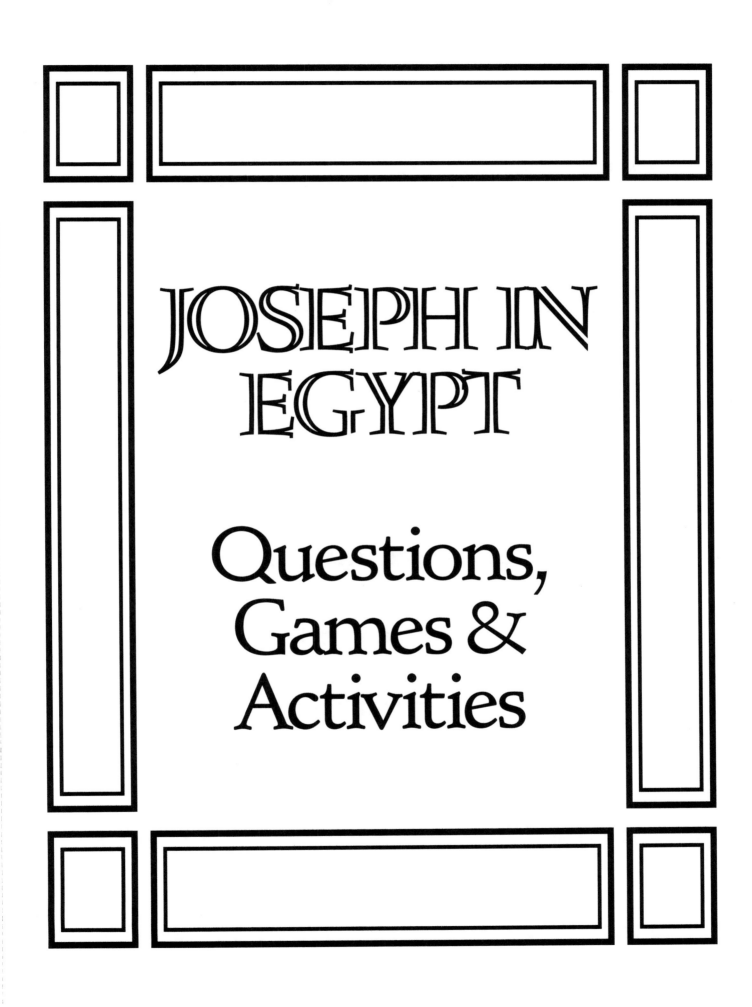

QUESTIONS

1. Who purchased Joseph to be his servant?
2. Was Joseph honest and trustworthy?
3. Why was Joseph cast into prison?
4. Did the jail keeper like Joseph?
5. What two members of Pharaoh's household were also cast into prison?
6. Who told Pharaoh that Joseph could interpret dreams?
7. What two things did Pharaoh dream about?
8. Who interpreted Pharaoh's dream?
9. What was the meaning of Pharaoh's dream?
10. What did Pharaoh do for Joseph?

CROSSWORD PUZZLE

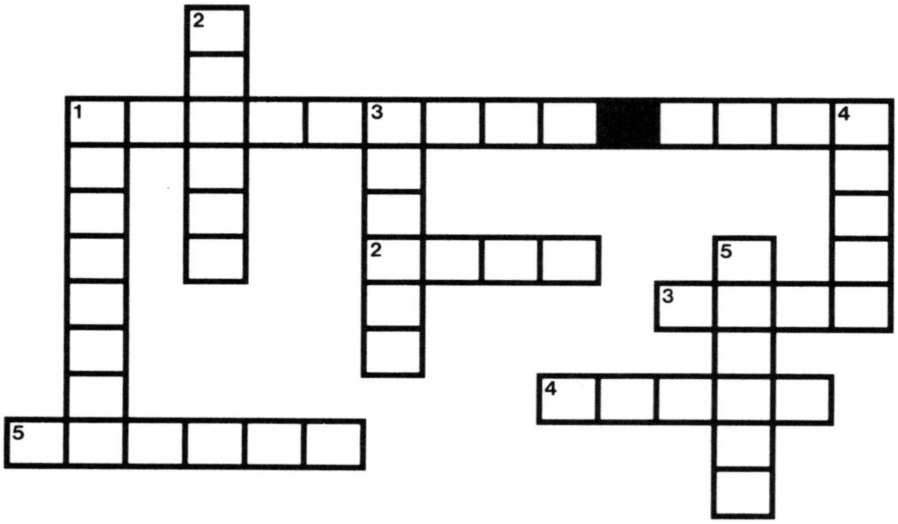

ACROSS:

1. Tried to tempt Joseph. (2 words)
2. What Pharaoh gave to Joseph.
3. What Potiphar's wife took from Joseph.
4. Was put to death by the Pharaoh.
5. What Joseph interpreted for the Butler and Baker.

DOWN:

1. Purchased Joseph as a slave.
2. Told Pharaoh that Joseph could interpret dreams.
3. Nationality of Joseph. (Also a language.)
4. Where story takes place.
5. Interpreted dreams.

Follow the Alphabet from A to Z to find out what this picture will be.
(For more of a challenge follow the Alphabet backwards.)

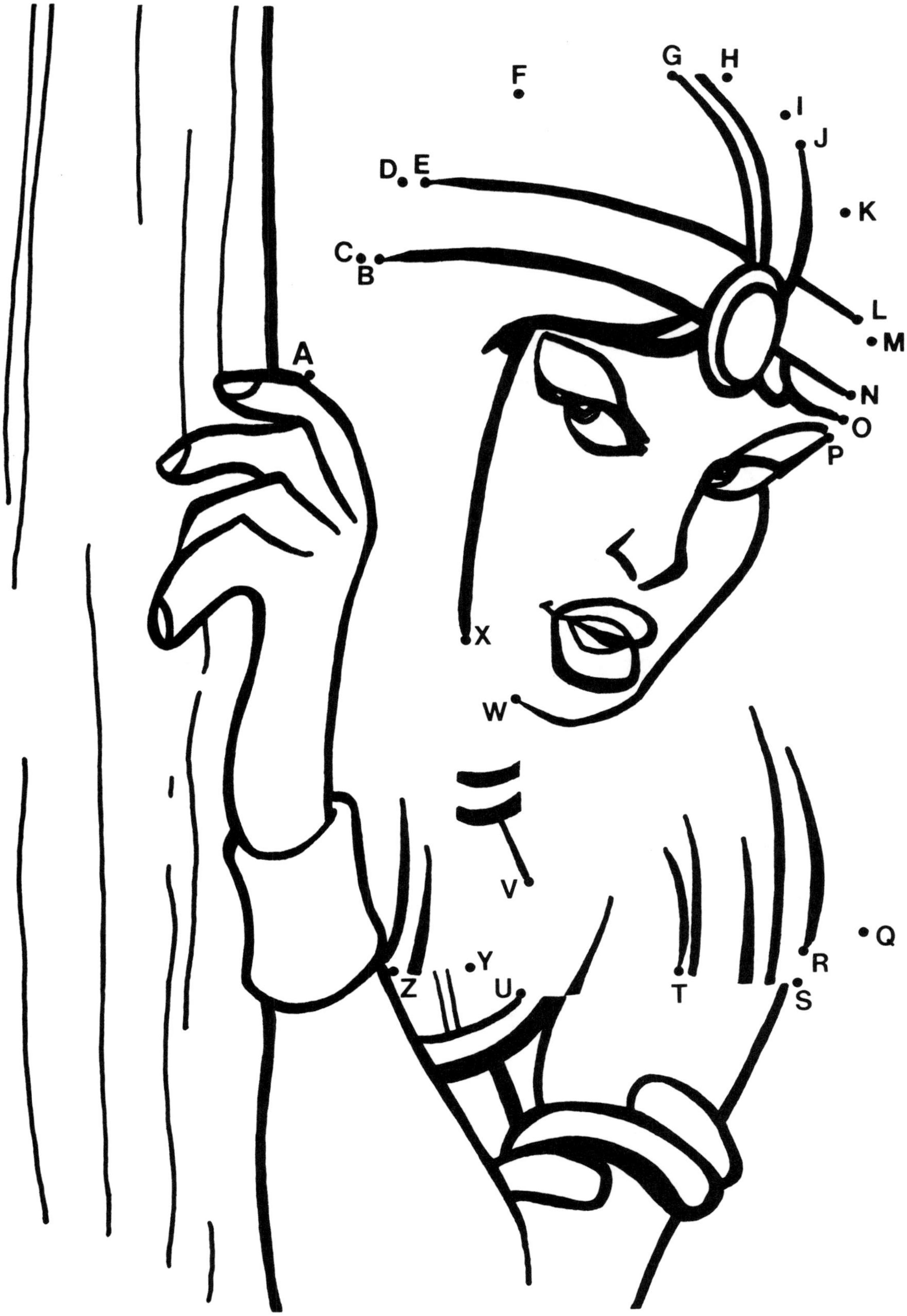

Family Entertainment Network, Inc.™ • P.O. Box 550759 • Dallas, Texas 75355-0759

(For more of a challenge follow the numbers backwards.)

Family Entertainment Network, Inc.™ • P.O. Box 550759 • Dallas, Texas 75355-0759

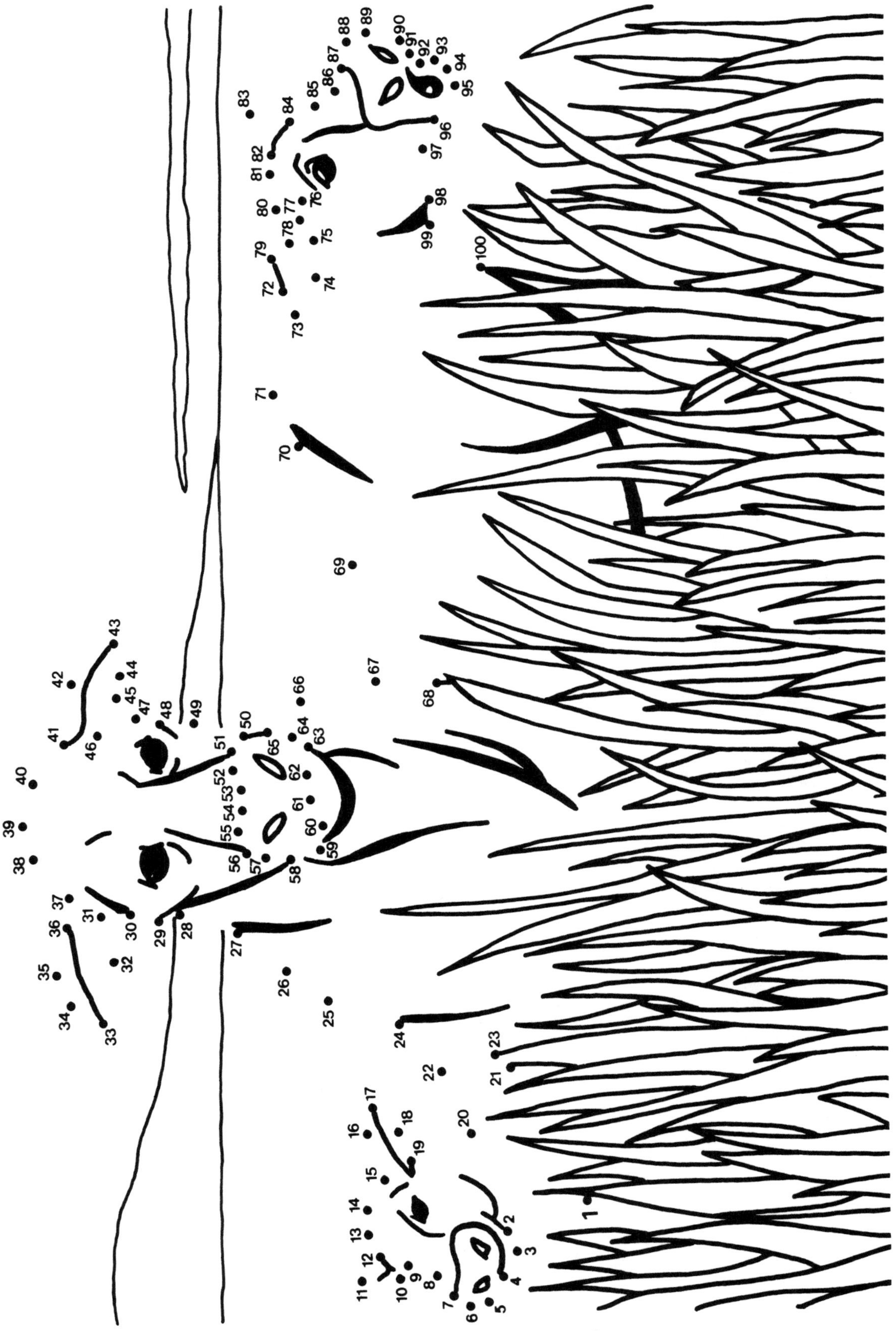

Family Entertainment Network, Inc.™ • P.O. Box 550759 • Dallas, Texas 75355-0759

WHICH PICTURE IS NOT LIKE THE OTHERS?

Look closely at each picture and circle the one that is not alike in each row.

1.

2.

3.

4.

5.

6.

7.

8.

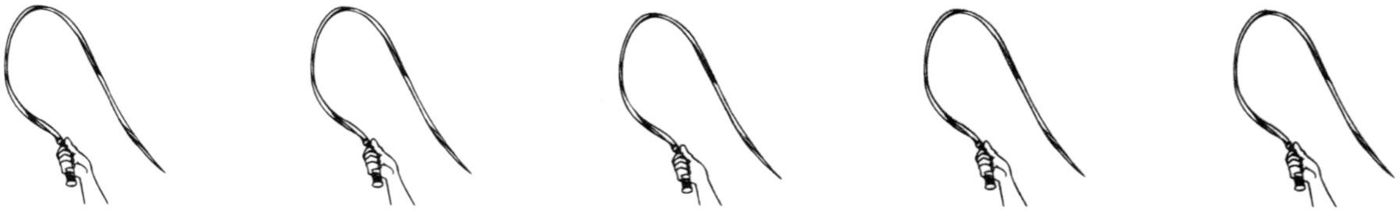

Family Entertainment Network, Inc.™ • P.O. Box 550759 • Dallas, Texas 75355-0759

WHICH PICTURE DOES NOT BELONG?

Look closely at each line below and circle the picture that doesn't fit in with the rest.

1.

2.

3.

POINTS TO PONDER

1. Joseph stayed faithful to God and did not complain, in spite of the many trials that he faced. When you face trials or problems in your own life, are you always faithful to God like Joseph was, or do you sometimes murmur and complain?

2. Joseph was close enough to God that he was given the ability to interpret dreams. Do you live your life closely enough to God to receive special gifts and powers as Joseph did?

WHAT'S WRONG WITH THIS PICTURE?

Circle the 16 things that are wrong with the picture below.
(Don't forget, some things had not been invented in Joseph's time.)

Family Entertainment Network, Inc.™ • P.O. Box 550759 • Dallas, Texas 75355-0759

COUNT THE STATUES

The Egyptian Pharaoh has misplaced some of his statues.
Help him find all 25 of them below.

WHICH HAPPENED FIRST?

Number each picture below in the order that they happened in the video. (For smaller children, xerox copy this page, and cut each picture apart. Then, have the child put them in the order that they happened in the video.)

______ ______ ______

WACKY WORDS

Unscramble the letters below to discover what words they spell.

1. INGAR ____________________
2. JPEHOS ____________________
3. VERSTNA ____________________
4. LREUR ____________________
5. PGEYT ____________________
6. EARSMD ____________________
7. KREBA ____________________
8. HARPOHA ____________________
9. MANFEI ____________________
10. RETOS ____________________

Family Entertainment Network, Inc.™ • P.O. Box 550759 • Dallas, Texas 75355-0759

WORD SEARCHES

Look both down and across to find the hidden words below:

L	G	F	A	M	I	N	E	P	A
S	J	Y	B	K	P	R	J	R	Q
P	O	T	I	P	H	A	R	A	U
F	S	T	O	I	X	N	V	Y	D
H	E	B	R	E	W	C	F	E	G
X	P	R	I	S	O	N	E	R	R
V	H	E	N	Z	C	Z	A	Q	A
D	U	W	G	F	M	H	S	G	I
Y	B	U	T	L	E	R	T	Y	N

BUTLER
FAMINE
FEAST
GRAIN
HEBREW
JOSEPH
POTIPHAR
PRAYER
PRISON
RING

BAKER
CORN
COWS
DREAM
EGYPT
RULER
SLAVE
WIFE

A	W	Y	D	R	E	A	M
R	I	D	J	Q	S	W	E
U	F	T	B	U	L	I	H
L	E	Z	H	X	A	E	C
E	G	Y	P	T	V	G	O
R	P	B	A	K	E	R	W
C	O	R	N	M	C	V	S

MATCHING GAME

Match each description on the left with the correct person on the right.

_____ 1. Interpreted dreams.

_____ 2 Told lies about Joseph.

_____ 3. Was killed by Pharaoh.

_____ 4. Purchased Joseph as a servant.

_____ 5. Had a dream about cows and corn.

A. Potiphar
B. Pharaoh
C. Baker
D. Joseph
E. Potiphar's Wife

Help the Pharaoh find Joseph.

Family Entertainment Network, Inc.™ • P.O. Box 550759 • Dallas, Texas 75355-0759

Help Joseph escape from Potiphar's wife.

Travel with Joseph through Egypt.

Family Entertainment Network, Inc.™ • P.O. Box 550759 • Dallas, Texas 75355-0759

WORD SEARCH

Look in every direction to find the hidden words below:

D	P	V	A	Q	X	G	E	N	J	U	F	Q	I	M	L	W	J	V	O
Y	E	R	F	J	M	H	S	O	Z	R	E	P	E	E	K	L	I	A	J
T	W	U	E	Z	G	J	O	S	E	P	H	I	N	E	G	Y	P	T	S
A	G	Z	M	K	D	W	C	R	K	K	Q	P	F	P	U	M	Z	R	T
F	R	O	G	U	A	P	H	Q	I	G	R	I	V	A	A	F	N	U	L
C	A	Y	U	K	V	B	Y	F	M	T	W	X	S	E	M	Y	C	S	H
L	S	T	C	T	L	X	A	S	I	S	T	O	R	W	H	J	Z	T	U
H	X	N	E	E	I	O	E	D	R	J	E	D	N	E	R	O	Q	W	E
P	D	E	I	R	W	S	N	A	C	T	L	V	K	R	P	A	Y	O	T
J	C	L	Q	P	J	Z	H	G	N	S	U	O	E	T	H	G	I	R	K
V	M	P	T	R	Y	P	L	M	Z	H	E	R	I	N	B	V	N	T	X
E	W	D	O	E	I	U	K	H	E	G	W	A	Q	U	Y	S	X	H	F
B	L	G	R	T	X	M	B	O	Y	E	D	Y	T	X	T	E	M	Y	Z
I	U	Q	O	N	I	Y	B	P	F	C	L	L	N	J	U	P	A	B	Q
M	F	P	X	I	V	P	T	Z	B	Z	E	I	P	R	N	R	G	R	A
S	H	W	C	A	E	I	H	I	Y	R	L	V	T	O	W	H	I	Y	S
B	T	F	V	S	A	F	P	A	P	I	M	X	S	E	T	Q	C	B	N
D	I	H	O	N	E	A	L	T	R	B	U	I	O	N	S	W	I	V	D
K	A	U	S	E	R	V	A	N	T	J	R	M	H	O	A	R	A	H	P
G	F	A	M	I	N	E	B	Y	L	P	K	C	G	P	F	S	N	I	A

BAKER
BUTLER
DREAM
EGYPTIANS
FAITHFUL
FAMINE
INTERPRET
ISHMEELITES
JAILKEEPER
JOSEPH IN EGYPT
MAGICIAN
PHARAOH
PLENTY
POTIPHAR
POTIPHAR'S WIFE
PRISON
RIGHTEOUS
SERVANT
SEVEN YEARS
TRUSTWORTHY

WHICH WORD DOES NOT BELONG?

Circle the one word in each row that does not belong with the others.

1. Dream	Cows	Horse	Corn
2. Mermaid	Famine	Seven Years	Plenty
3. Potiphar's Wife	Interpreter	Dreams	Joseph
4. Butler	Potiphar	Pharoah	Baker
5. Joseph	Triangle	Egypt	Prison

WHICH TWO MATCH?

Look closely at each line below and circle the two pictures that look exactly alike.

1.

2.

PICTURE THIS

Color in every space that has a dot to find out what the picture is.

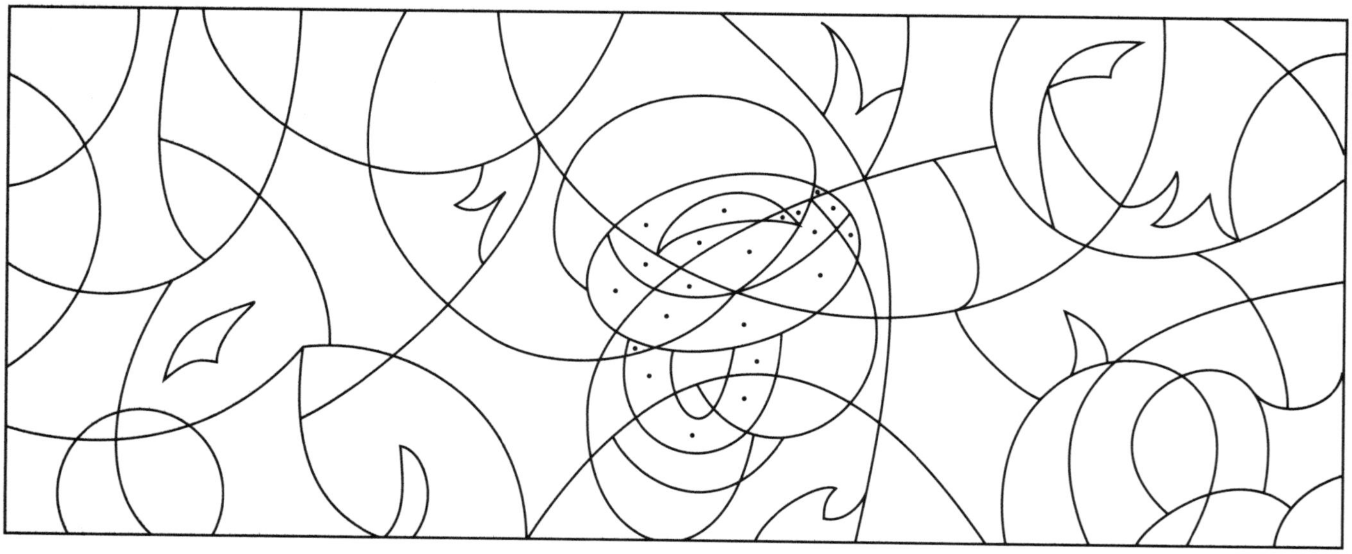

Family Entertainment Network, Inc.™ • P.O. Box 550759 • Dallas, Texas 75355-0759

WHAT'S DIFFERENT?

There are 8 differences between these two pictures.
See how many you can find by circling the picture on the right.

There are 9 differences between these two pictures.
See how many you can find by circling the picture on the right.

HIDDEN OBJECTS

Find the objects hidden in the picture below.

Bone	Elephant's Head	Frosted Cake	Pencil	Orange Slice
Bow Tie	Fish	Hamburger	Pipe	Tree Leaf
Carrot	Four Leaf Clover	Monkey	Playing Card	Witch's Profile

Family Entertainment Network, Inc.™ • P.O. Box 550759 • Dallas, Texas 75355-0759

GATHER THE GRAIN

Help Joseph gather the grain from every road in Egypt
and take it to the store rooms, without retracing his steps.

(See “Game Cards” on page 38)

(See "Game Cards" on page 38)

IDEAS FOR GROUP ACTIVITIES

DRAWING GAME: The group is divided into teams, and various scenes or people from the video are written on slips of paper. The teams then alternate taking the slips of paper out of a bowl and drawing the mentioned scene or person on a chalkboard or paper until team members guess what the scene or person is. A time limit should be given, and if the team is not able to guess the scene in the allotted amount of time, no point is earned. The other team is then given a chance to steal the point.

CHARADES: The group is divided into teams, and various scenes from the video are acted out. Points are scored for each correct answer.

QUESTION AND ANSWER GAME: The questions are copied on a copy machine, cut apart, and placed in a bowl. The group is divided into teams, and each team takes turns drawing the questions out of the bowl. Points are scored by correctly answering each question. If the team drawing the question cannot answer it correctly, the opposing team gets a chance to steal the point.

MATCHING GAME: The names from the matching game are put on an overhead or chalkboard, and the descriptions are copied on a copy machine, cut apart, and placed in a bowl. The group is divided into teams, and each team alternates taking a description out of the bowl and matching it with the correct name or item on the board. Points are scored by correctly matching the description with the name. If the team drawing the description cannot answer it correctly, the opposing team gets a chance to steal the point.

WHO AM I?: Qualities and descriptions of personalities in the video are read aloud one at a time. In this game, teams do not take turns; Instead, a point is scored by the **first** team that is able to name the person being described. For example; Joseph could be described as follows: Sold as a slave; servant to Potiphar; interpreted dreams; etc.

THE DESCRIPTION GAME: Names of various personalities in the video are written on slips of paper and placed in a bowl. The group is divided into teams, and each team takes turns drawing names out of the bowl and describing each personality to their team members. Once the team guesses correctly, the team member draws another name from the bowl. Each team is given 1 minute per turn to describe as many personalities as possible. Points are given for each correct answer. For example; If a team member drew "Joseph" out of the bowl, the clues suggested in **"Who Am I?"** could be given to help team members guess correctly. If the time allotment is not up by the time the team guesses correctly, the member draws another name from the bowl and continues until their time allotment is out.

TWENTY QUESTIONS: One member of the group is "it" and thinks of a person, place or thing from the video without telling anyone what the word is. The rest of the group asks him/her yes or no questions trying to figure out the word. If they fail to figure out the answer within 20 questions, the person who is "it" wins.

HANG-MAN: One member of the group is "it" and thinks of a word or phrase having to do with the video. He then puts a dash for every letter in the word or phrase on a paper or chalkboard. The rest of the group takes turns guessing letters. If a guessed letter is in the word or phrase, it is written into the corresponding blank on the board. If a guessed letter is not contained in the word or phase, one part of the hang-man is drawn. If the hang-man is completed before the group finishes filling in the blanks, the person who is "it" wins.

GAME CARDS: Using a copy machine, make at least 2 copies of each page of "Game Cards" on card stock. Color them, if you wish, and then, laminate each page and cut apart. These game cards can be used for several different games such as "Concentration", "Fish", different versions of **Which Happened First** (page 26), etc.

ANSWER KEY

for
Questions,
Games,
and
Activities

ANSWER KEY

Questions, Games & Activities

Answers to Questions:

1. Potiphar. (Genesis 37:36; Genesis 39:1)
2. Yes. (Genesis 39:3-6)
3. When Joseph refused to be unfaithful to his master, Potiphar's wife told lies about Joseph to Potiphar, and Potiphar had him cast into prison. (Genesis 39:7-20)
4. Yes. (Genesis 39:21-23)
5. The Butler and the Baker. (Genesis 40:1-3)
6. The Butler. (Genesis 41:9-13)
7. Cows (Kine) and corn. (Genesis 41:1-7)
8. Joseph. (Genesis 41:14-32)
9. Pharaoh's dream was a warning that there would be seven years of plenty in Egypt followed by seven years of famine.(Genesis 41:14-32)
10. He made Joseph ruler over Egypt under him and gave him his ring. (Genesis 41:39-45)

Answers to Crossword Puzzle:

Down

1. Potiphar
2. Butler
3. Hebrew
4. Egypt
5. Joseph

Across

1. Potiphars Wife
2. Ring
3. Coat
4. Baker
5. Dreams

Answers to Which Picture Is Not Like the Others?

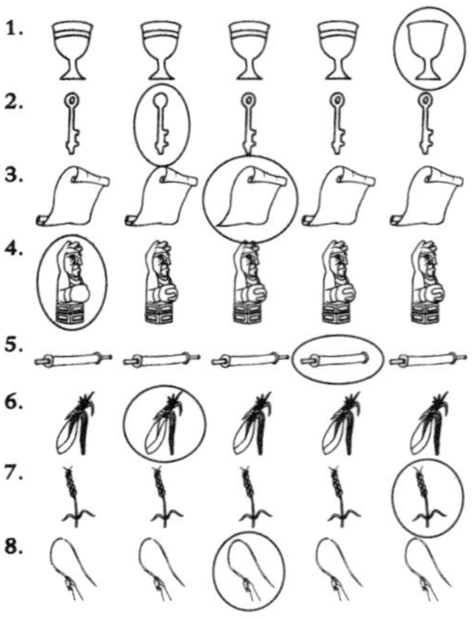

Answers to Which Picture Does Not Belong:

Answers to What Is Wrong With This Picture:

Answers to Count the Statues:

Answers to Which Happened First?

2 1 3

Answers to Wacky Words:

1. Grain
2. Joseph
3. Servant
4. Ruler
5. Egypt
6. Dreams
7. Baker
8. Pharaoh
9. Famine
10. Store

ANSWER KEY

Questions, Games & Activities

Answers to Word Searches:

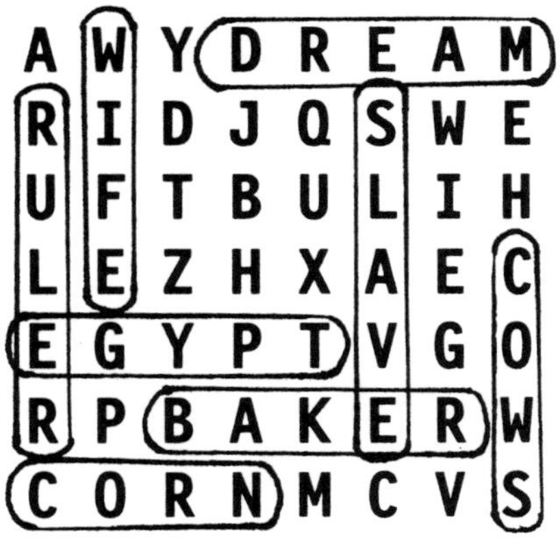

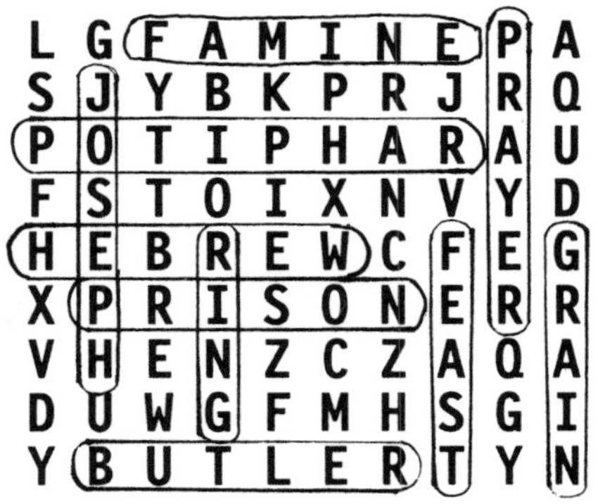

Answers to Matching Game:

1. D
2. E
3. C
4. A
5. B

Answer to "Help Pharaoh find Joseph" Maze:

Help the Pharaoh find Joseph.
Start

Answer to "Help Joseph Escape" Maze:

Help Joseph escape from Potiphar's wife.

Answer to "Travel with Joseph" Maze:

Travel with Joseph through Egypt.

Answers to Word Search:

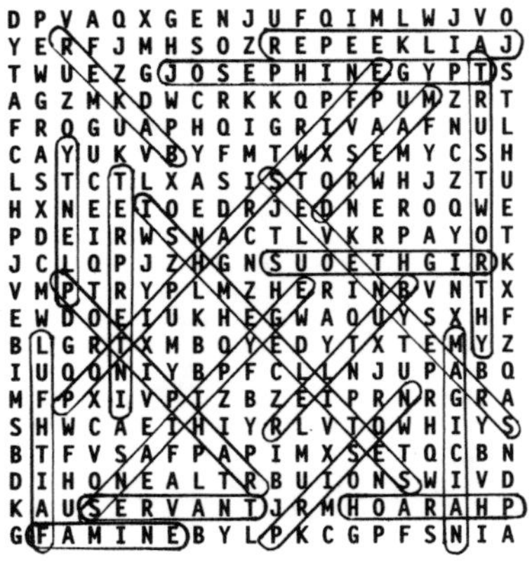

Answers to Which Word Does Not Belong?

1. Dream	Cows	**Horse**	Corn
2. **Mermaid**	Famine	Seven Years	Plenty
3. **Potiphar's Wife**	Interpreter	Dreams	Joseph
4. Butler	**Potiphar**	Pharaoh	Baker
5. Joseph	**Triangle**	Egypt	Prison

ANSWER KEY

Questions, Games & Activities

Answers to Which Two Match:

Answers to Fill in the Dots:

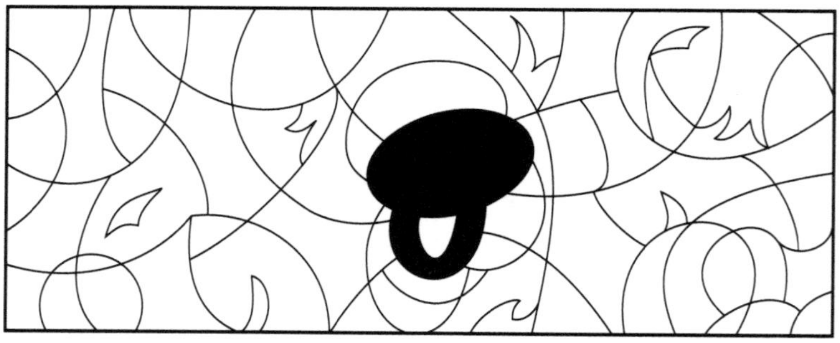

Answers to What's Different:

Answers to Hidden Objects:

Answer to Gather the Grain:

(This is only one way to solve this puzzle. See if you can find more.)

Certificate of Achievement

This certifies that

____

has mastered the "Joseph in Egypt" Activity Book from
Family Entertainment Network, Inc. by successfully completing all of the
questions, games and activities found herein.

"O love the Lord, all ye his saints: for the Lord
preserveth the faithful, and plentifully rewardeth the proud doer."

-Psalms 31:23

Stephen W. Griffin
Stephen W. Griffin
President

____
Dated